CROSSWORD AMERICA

THE PRESIDENTS

Written by Cathryn Long

Illustrations by Larry Nolte

LOWELL HOUSE JUVENILE

LOS ANGELES

NTC/Contemporary Publishing Group

Published by Lowell House
A division of NTC/Contemporary Publishing Group, Inc.
4255 West Touhy Avenue, Lincolnwood (Chicago), Illinois 60712 U.S.A.

Managing Director and Publisher: Jack Artenstein
Director of Publishing Services: Rena Copperman
Editorial Director: Brenda Pope-Ostrow
Editor: Joanna Siebert
Designer: Carolyn Wendt
Cover Designer: Treesha Runnells Vaux

Lowell House books can be purchased at special discounts
when ordered in bulk for premiums and special sales.
Contact Customer Service at the above address,
or call 1-800-323-4900.

Printed and bound in the United States of America

Library of Congress Catalog Card Number: 99-75595

ISBN: 0-7373-0364-6

PHOTO CREDITS:
National Archives: Presidents' formal portraits on pp. 1, 7, 9, 11, 13, 15,
17, 19, 21, 23, 25, 27, 29, 31, 33, 35, 37, 39, 41, 43, 45, 47, 49, 51, 53, and 61
Bush Presidential Materials Project: Presidents' formal portraits on pp. 55, 57, and 59
Library of Congress: pp. 25, 29, 33, 37, 39, and 61
Franklin D. Roosevelt Library: p. 43
Harry S. Truman Library: p. 45
Dwight D. Eisenhower Library/U.S. Navy: p. 47
Morgan Collection/Archive Photos: p. 49
Lyndon Baines Johnson Library: p. 51
Jimmy Carter Library: p. 55
Ronald Reagan Library: p. 57
George Bush Presidential Library: p. 59

Manufactured in the United States of America

RCP 10 9 8 7 6 5 4 3 2

CONTENTS

To the Teacher and Parent

The crossword puzzles in this book offer a quick look into the lives and accomplishments of the presidents of the United States, from George Washington to the very latest person in the White House. You can use the puzzles to introduce or enhance history lessons, or to compare holders of this office. Above all, these small puzzles are meant as a fun way to remember names and facts about the nation's leaders. Of course, not all aspects of biography or history could be included in each puzzle; instead, these puzzles are meant to be triggers for curiosity. One good use of the puzzles is to make them take-off points for look-it-up sessions in the library, and for writing of reports or longer biographies.

You may want to take a few minutes before passing out the puzzles to review with students the way the presidency fits in with the other parts of American government. Students should be aware that presidents have to work with Congress in creating laws, for instance. They should also be aware that political parties help determine who gets to run for president and what the policies of a president will be.

To find the clues and complete each puzzle, students will need to *read and understand* the introductory paragraphs, as well as *locate information in illustrations* that accompany each puzzle. In addition, students can *locate an appropriate word on the alphabetical list of words* provided with each puzzle as another aid in solving the puzzle. If your students are unfamiliar with this type of puzzle, review with them the word numbering system and the way "across" words give clues for "down" words, and vice versa.

Some of these puzzles focus on just one president, and some cover two or three. If you would like more coverage of a president, you may want to have students do some research and create their own puzzles, complete with clues. Puzzle makers can then exchange their creations.

For the Puzzle Player

(Students or anyone else interested in the American presidents!)

Do you know which president nearly doubled the size of the United States? Who was the first president to speak Spanish well? Which one kept an alligator for a pet? This book will help you learn these and many other facts about the U.S. presidents by solving crossword puzzles. All the clues you need to solve each puzzle are included with it. There are three ways to find clues:

1. Read the story about the president or presidents that comes with the puzzle.
2. Look carefully at the pictures. Some contain important clues.
3. Look for the right word in the word list below the puzzle.

In this book, the presidents are in chronological order, but you can solve the puzzles in any order you wish. Have fun learning about all the presidents in this volume of *Crossword America!*

GEORGE WASHINGTON

I t was hard to miss George Washington in a crowd. He stood six feet two inches tall, and even his shoes were a big size thirteen. Born on a Virginia farm, he always loved dogs and horses. When he was a boy, his schoolwork was patchy, but Washington learned enough to find work as a surveyor measuring land. By the age of twenty-one, Washington had joined the Virginia militia.

The military proved to be the right career for George Washington. He showed courage and good judgment in fighting for Britain in the last of the French and Indian Wars. In 1759, Washington married a wealthy young widow named Martha.

When the colonies rebelled against Britain, George Washington seemed to be a natural choice to lead the fight for independence. General Washington and his army faced many hardships during the Revolutionary War. After the colonies won, George and Martha Washington retired to their home at Mount Vernon. Within a few years, however, Washington was asked to be chairman of the convention that would create a national constitution. In 1789, the new position of president of the United States was given to Washington. It was the first and last time all the presidential electors (the representatives who elect the president) voted for the same person.

Washington appointed the best people he could find to his cabinet, or group of presidential advisers. However, his advisers often disagreed. Secretary of State Thomas Jefferson favored farmers and more power for the states. Alexander Hamilton, secretary of the treasury, wanted the nation to serve merchants through a centralized government. Washington tried to remain impartial but agreed most often with Hamilton.

Washington faced an important challenge when some farmers in Pennsylvania refused to pay a federal tax on whiskey. The president called up troops to end the Whiskey Rebellion. The farmers backed down and accepted the right of the national government to govern and tax as needed.

While Washington was successful in foreign affairs, he worked hard to keep America neutral, or free from any alliance that might result in war. He retired to Mount Vernon after two terms, already legendary as the Father of His Country.

Across

1. Washington fought for the British against the Indians and this country.
2. Washington's home colony or state
5. Washington's position at the Constitutional Convention
10. Representatives who elect the president
11. Washington's secretary of the treasury
13. Animal Washington loved (besides dogs)
14. Money paid to the government; cause of the Whiskey Rebellion
15. Washington's army rank during the Revolutionary War
16. Alcoholic beverage made from grain; early American farmers did not want it taxed

Down

1. Male parent; the role Washington is said to have in relation to the nation
2. Second word in the name of Washington's home
3. Opposite of short; what Washington was

WASHINGTON
1789–1797

4. Thomas Jefferson often sided with this group of citizens.
6. Not taking sides; the condition Washington wanted for the nation
7. Washington wore false ones.
8. Jefferson was Washington's secretary of _____.
9. Term for the president's group of advisers
12. First name of Washington's wife

It is a myth that George Washington's false teeth were made out of wood. They were made from other teeth—those of humans and animals—and also from tusks!

Word List

cabinet	farmers	Hamilton	state	Vernon
chairman	father	horse	tall	Virginia
electors	France	Martha	tax	whiskey
	general	neutral	teeth	

JOHN ADAMS

His enemies called him "His Rotundity" and laughed at his stuck-up manners. Yet John Adams worked hard all his life to shape and serve the nation he loved.

Adams grew up on a Massachusetts farm. He was educated at Harvard University and became a lawyer. As a young man, Adams took on the difficult task of defending the British soldiers who fired into a mob of colonists in the Boston Massacre. He entered the Massachusetts legislature and was caught up in the fight against Britain for colonial rights. Adams was an important member of the Continental Congress, and after urging Thomas Jefferson to write the first draft of the Declaration of Independence, Adams continued to play an important role in the making of that historic document. He spent several years in Europe working as a diplomat for the new United States.

Because of his political career, Adams was often separated from his wife, Abigail. They wrote to each other frequently. "Remember the ladies," Abigail once wrote, "and be more generous and favorable to them than your ancestors!"

Soon after Adams returned from Europe, he was elected vice president under George Washington. He disliked the job much of the time because he had so little power. After eight years, though, he was in a position to be elected president.

The presidency proved to be hard for Adams. His toughest job was maintaining peace with France. He managed to do so, in part, by creating a navy that would threaten anyone planning to attack an American ship. However, keeping the peace did not help Adams's political career. Alexander Hamilton and other members of the Federalist Party had wanted to fight France. They withdrew their support for Adams and he lost the election in 1800.

John and Abigail Adams enjoyed a long retirement in Massachusetts. Adams's favorite activity was reading. "You will never be alone with a poet in your pocket," he declared. As a very old man, he was overjoyed when his son John Quincy Adams became president.

Across

4. First name of Adams's wife
5. Adams's biggest challenge was keeping the peace with this country.
8. Adams liked to keep the work of this kind of writer in his pocket.
9. Adams worked with Jefferson on the Declaration of _____.
11. First word in the name of Adams's position in Washington's administration
12. Adams grew up on one in the countryside.
14. Adams served as a member of this government body in the Massachusetts colony.
16. Because he was short and overweight, Adams was nicknamed "His _____."
17. As a lawyer, Adams defended the British soldiers involved in the Boston _____.

Down

ADAMS
1797–1801

1. Number of terms Adams served as president
2. Adams's home colony or state
3. Adams's profession
5. Party that withdrew support for Adams after one term
6. Adams was the first president to live in the _____ House in Washington, D.C.
7. Adams attended this university.
10. Initials of Adams's son who became a president
13. Adams served as a diplomat there.
15. Number of years Adams served as vice president

Adams was the first president to live in the White House.

Word List

Abigail	farm	Independence	Massachusetts	Rotundity
eight	Federalist	JQA	Massacre	vice
Europe	France	lawyer	one	White
	Harvard	legislature	poet	

THOMAS JEFFERSON

Thomas Jefferson was born on a prosperous plantation in Virginia. Jefferson's accomplishments—in and out of politics—are amazing! He mastered many languages and was an expert on plants and crops, music, fine food, and Indian artifacts. He was trained in the law. Jefferson designed his own home, called Monticello, and the buildings at the University of Virginia, which he also founded. He created money for the United States and invented the swivel chair, among other things.

At age twenty-six, Jefferson became a member of the colonial legislature of Virginia. Although he did not fight in the Revolutionary War, Jefferson was an important member of the Continental Congress. He was the chief author of the Declaration of Independence. After the war, he wrote a statute, or law, of religious freedom for Virginia. He was a U.S. ambassador, or minister, to France when the Constitution was written, but he returned to serve in the first cabinet as President Washington's secretary of state. After serving as John Adams's vice president, Jefferson was elected president.

Jefferson headed the new Democratic Republican Party, an earlier form of today's Democratic Party. Jefferson and his party thought that the national government should be small and not interfere much in private affairs. As president, Jefferson spent little money and cut the budgets of the army and navy.

Although Jefferson thought the government should stay within the bounds set by the Constitution, he could not resist buying the Louisiana Territory from France for the bargain price of $15 million. With the Louisiana Purchase, Jefferson nearly doubled the size of the United States.

After eight years in office, Jefferson retired to Monticello. On July 4, 1826, the fiftieth anniversary of the Declaration of Independence, Jefferson (and his old colleague John Adams) died.

Across

3. Two-letter abbreviation of Jefferson's home colony or state
5. Jefferson founded the Democratic _____ Party.
7. Jefferson did not personally fight in this.
8. Jefferson reduced spending for this fighting force.
12. Jefferson died _____ years after the Declaration of Independence was written.
13. President for whom Jefferson served as vice president
15. Jefferson made a good deal for the Louisiana _____.
16. Jefferson's home
18. Opposite of big; what Jefferson thought government should be

Down

1. Jefferson was chief author of the _____ of Independence.
2. Initials of one man Jefferson sent to explore the Louisiana Territory

4. Jefferson was a U.S. _____ in France when the Constitution was written.

6. Jefferson's family business

9. Jefferson invented a form of this for the nation.

10. Under Adams, Jefferson served as ____ president.

11. Jefferson was trained in this field.

14. Jefferson wrote an important Virginia law to protect the religious kind of this.

17. Number of terms Jefferson served as president

JEFFERSON
1801–1809

The Lewis and Clark Expedition

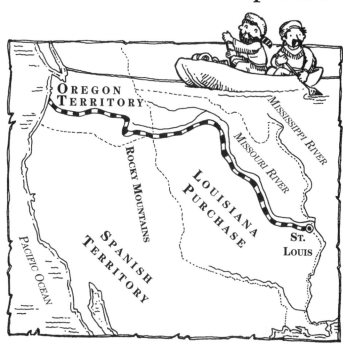

President Jefferson sent Meriwether Lewis and William Clark to explore the Louisiana Territory after its purchase.

11

JAMES MADISON, JAMES MONROE, AND JOHN QUINCY ADAMS

James Madison and James Monroe were the last leaders of the American Revolution to become presidents. John Quincy Adams, son of the nation's second president, represented a new generation.

James Madison helped create the U.S. Constitution. His notes on the secret debates over how to shape the U.S. government are an invaluable part of American history. In addition, Madison wrote the Bill of Rights, the first ten amendments to the Constitution.

Thomas Jefferson appointed Madison secretary of state (Monroe and John Quincy Adams later held the same job for different presidents). France and Britain were already at war, and the Democratic Republican Party wanted the nation to join France in the fight. After he was elected president, Madison declared war against Britain. In 1814, the British attacked Washington, D.C., burning the Executive Mansion (later called the White House) and other buildings, and forcing members of the government to flee for a time. In spite of the turmoil, Madison's life in Washington was a social success, thanks mostly to his wife, Dolley, who loved hosting parties. The War of 1812 ended in 1815 and yielded "The Star-Spangled Banner," a song that became the national anthem.

James Monroe received some credit for postwar contentment. One newspaper nicknamed his time in office the "era of good feeling." During Monroe's administration, the United States acquired Florida from Spain. Spain and other European countries later threatened to retake their former colonies in Central and South America. Monroe issued the Monroe Doctrine, a document warning the countries of Europe not to create colonies in the Americas.

As a member of Monroe's cabinet, John Quincy Adams helped create the Monroe Doctrine and acquire Florida. However, Adams did not accomplish much during his time in office, because the majority of representatives in Congress were politically opposed to him. President Adams went swimming in the Potomac River every morning when the weather was good. He also kept an alligator as a pet! John Quincy Adams was not elected to a second term as president, but he did serve as a congressman after he left office. In that position, he worked against slavery and for people's rights and helped found the Smithsonian Institution in Washington, D.C.

Across

1. Monroe's time in office was sometimes called the "era of good _____."
5. Madison kept notes on the creation of this document: the U.S. _____.
7. The War of 1812 was favored by the Democratic Republican _____.
9. First name of Madison's wife
11. Mandate to keep European powers out of the Americas: the Monroe _____
12. Initials of John Quincy Adams's father

13. Language spoken in the country that burned the capital during the War of 1812
15. Animal kept as a pet by John Quincy Adams
16. Country from which Monroe gained Florida

MADISON
1809–1817

Down

1. Southernmost state, which once belonged to Spain
2. Madison spent much of his time at the Constitutional Convention making these.
3. Madison, Monroe, and Adams all served as secretary of this department.
4. "The Star-Spangled Banner," written during Madison's presidency, is called the national _____.
6. Washington, D.C., institution that John Quincy Adams helped found
7. River where John Quincy Adams went swimming each day
8. John Quincy Adams could do little during his presidency because the majority in this government body was politically opposed to him.
10. Madison wrote the ____ of Rights.
14. Madison declared this against Britain.

MONROE
1817–1825

ADAMS
1825–1829

Word List

alligator	Congress	English	notes	Spain
anthem	Constitution	feeling	Party	state
Bill	Doctrine	Florida	Potomac	war
	Dolley	JA	Smithsonian	

ANDREW JACKSON

They called him "Old Hickory" because he was so tough. Andrew Jackson was born in a log cabin along the border of North and South Carolina and barely learned to read. At the age of thirteen, he became a messenger for the militia in the Revolutionary War and was captured by the British. When he refused to clean a British officer's boots, the man slashed Jackson's hand with a sword. The scar remained for life—and so did Jackson's fighting spirit. He fought Indians along the frontier and had become a general in the U.S. Army by the War of 1812. Old Hickory led American troops to victory over the British in the battle of New Orleans, and became famous for it nationwide. It did not seem to matter that the war had actually ended before the battle took place, as news of the peace had not arrived in time.

Jackson's supporters wanted him to be president after Monroe, but Jackson lost to John Quincy Adams when the close election had to be decided in the House of Representatives. Four years later, Jackson won. His wife, Rachel, died just before Jackson took office. His frontier followers showed up to celebrate his inauguration. The crowd muddied White House furniture, broke glasses, and overturned the punch. Refined Americans were horrified, but Jackson's friends called him the first "people's president."

In office, Jackson insisted he was there to represent the people, not to go along with Congress. He was the first president to veto many bills. He pushed for what he wanted, such as the removal of Indian tribes from the eastern United States in the 1830s. He also strengthened the hand of the federal government against the states. When South Carolina refused to obey a tariff law, he was prepared to use force—until the state agreed to a compromise. After two terms, Jackson retired to Tennessee, as popular as when he was elected.

Across

5. Jackson defeated the British at the battle of New _____.
6. Initials of the man who won the first time Jackson ran for president
7. Jackson fought in more than one of these.
8. Ceremony at the beginning of a presidency; Jackson's was riotous
12. Age at which Jackson served as messenger for the Revolutionary militia
14. Jackson forced Indian tribes from this part of the United States to move west of the Mississippi.
15. Jackson made officials in South _____ obey federal tariff law.
17. Uneducated, Jackson could barely do this.
18. Jackson was the first president to use this power often.

Down

1. As a young man, Jackson fought these people.
2. Many of Jackson's friends from this area came to the inauguration.

3. Jackson was born in this kind of house.
4. Tax on imported goods, which some states did not want to pay
9. First name of Jackson's wife
10. Job Jackson had as a boy during the Revolutionary War
11. Rank Jackson attained in the U.S. Army
13. Mark on Jackson's hand, caused by a British officer
16. First word in Jackson's nickname

**JACKSON
1829–1837**

Jackson fought more than one duel during his lifetime.

Word List

cabin	eastern	Indians	Orleans	tariff
Carolina	frontier	JQA	Rachel	thirteen
duel	general	messenger	read	veto
	inauguration	Old	scar	

MARTIN VAN BUREN, WILLIAM HENRY HARRISON, AND JOHN TYLER

Martin Van Buren was the first president to be born an American citizen (presidents before him were born British citizens), yet he spoke Dutch at home! That's because his family was part of the old Dutch settlement of Kinderhook, New York.

Van Buren was a good politician. He was able to "ride Andrew Jackson's coattails," rising from vice president during Jackson's second term to president in 1837. Van Buren's election campaign was the first in which rallies, sing-alongs, and slogans played an important role.

Van Buren ran into big trouble once he became president. The country was plunged into an economic depression. Too many people had borrowed money to buy land, expecting the value of land to rise. When it did not, they lost money. Banks and businesses closed, and many workers lost their jobs. Even though the depression was caused mostly by overspeculation and a natural economic downturn, it hurt the president's image. Van Buren was defeated after his first term by William Henry Harrison.

Harrison was an Ohio general, famous for winning the battle against Chief Tecumseh at the Tippecanoe River. Known as "Old Tippecanoe," Harrison ran for president with vice presidential candidate John Tyler. Harrison became ill while giving his inauguration speech in cold weather. It was the longest inauguration speech in American history—one hour and forty-five minutes! Afterward, Harrison said, "I am ill, very ill." He died one month after his inauguration.

Subsequently, John Tyler became president. Although Tyler was a Whig, as Harrison had been, he did not agree with most of the party's policies. The Whigs favored central government, while Tyler wanted the states to have more rights. He vetoed his own party's bills, including one that would create a national bank. However, just three days before he left office, Tyler did sign a bill to make Texas part of the United States.

Across

2. Tyler wanted more rights for these.
5. Initials of the position Van Buren held in Jackson's administration
6. Site of the battle from which Harrison got his nickname
9. Harrison was president for one _____.
10. Tyler signed a bill dealing with this state.
11. Language Van Buren spoke at home
12. After his inauguration, Harrison admitted he was _____.
14. Tyler opposed the creation of this kind of bank.
16. Van Buren's hometown

Down

1. Economic problem the nation faced while Van Buren was in office
2. Snappy sayings; these were an important part of Van Buren's campaign
3. Van Buren lost for a second term because he could not improve the state of this.
4. Harrison's inaugural one was the longest in history.
6. Name of the Indian chief defeated by Harrison at Tippecanoe
7. Van Buren was the first president not born a British _____.
8. Harrison's political party
13. Dance Tyler brought to the White House
15. The depression of Van Buren's time was partly caused by borrowing to buy this.

Tyler introduced the polka to people at White House parties.

VAN BUREN
1837–1841

HARRISON
1841

TYLER
1841–1845

Word List

citizen	economy	month	speech	Tippecanoe
depression	ill	national	states	VP
Dutch	Kinderhook	polka	Tecumseh	Whig
	land	slogans	Texas	

JAMES POLK, ZACHARY TAYLOR, AND MILLARD FILLMORE

James Polk was chosen by the Democrats partly because no one knew him well enough to be his enemy. He was the first dark-horse, or unlikely to win, presidential candidate. No alcohol was allowed in the White House during Polk's administration. He is said to have preferred water instead.

By the mid-1800s, American pioneers wanted to move west freely, but Mexico and Britain still claimed some of the land. Polk helped arrange an agreement with Britain to divide the Oregon Territory into two sections, one of which would become part of Canada. However, he could not pry California away from Mexico. In fact, the United States and Mexico were still disputing about the recently annexed Texas. Polk sent U.S. troops to Mexico, where they were attacked by Mexican forces. American troops easily defeated the Mexican army, and Polk arranged to pay Mexico for land that would one day become part of California, Nevada, Utah, Arizona, New Mexico, and Wyoming.

Polk retired after only one term and died soon after he left office. Polk's political rivals, the Whigs, nominated the army general whom Polk had sent to Mexico. His name was Zachary Taylor, also known as "Old Rough and Ready." Taylor did not have any political experience before entering office. Taylor brought his horse, Old Whitey, to the White House, where it grazed on the lawn. He focused on the major issue of the day: whether California and New Mexico would ban slavery when they entered the Union. The Southern states were afraid this would upset the balance of states and threatened to leave the Union. Taylor favored slavery, but he told Congress that he would lead an army against the Southern states if they tried to destroy the Union.

On July 4, 1850, President Taylor fell ill with stomach distress. He died five days later of cholera. Vice President Millard Fillmore, from New York, became president.

Fillmore was opposed to slavery, but he wanted to preserve the Union. He approved the Compromise of 1850, which had been proposed by Congress to relieve tensions between the North and the South. Among other things, the agreement allowed California to enter the Union as a free state, without slavery. It also set forth the Fugitive Slave Law, which required every state to allow the arrest and return of runaway slaves. Many Northerners were upset because this "compromise" seemed to favor slavery. Some Southerners were distressed that the federal government was now passing legislation on slavery rather than leaving it up to the states.

Across

3. An agreement in which each side gives up a little; Congress reached one in 1850
4. Taylor told Southerners from this body that if they left the Union, he would lead an army against them.
8. The _____ Slave Law was part of the Compromise of 1850.

9. This territory was split between the United States and Britain during Polk's administration.
11. Preferred drink in James Polk's White House
13. Two-letter abbreviation of a Southwestern state in the region bought during Polk's presidency
14. Some of the Oregon country became part of this northern neighbor of the United States.
15. This issue divided Americans more and more in the mid-1800s.
16. President Taylor's war horse, Old Whitey, liked this part of the White House.

Down

1. An unlikely to win candidate, like Polk, is called a _____ horse.
2. Initials of a state made from land Polk bought from Mexico
3. When Mexico refused to sell this region, Polk wanted to make war.
4. Anger over laws protecting slavery helped lead to this war.
5. President Taylor died five days after his _____ was upset.
6. Another word for *fugitive*
7. Taylor's favored career was in this U.S. organization.
10. State just east of California containing land that was obtained by Polk from Mexico
12. Taylor's nickname was "Old Rough and _____."

POLK
1845–1849

TAYLOR
1849–1850

FILLMORE
1850–1853

Word List

army	Canada	dark	NM	slavery
AZ	Civil	Fugitive	Oregon	stomach
California	compromise	lawn	Ready	water
	Congress	Nevada	runaway	

FRANKLIN PIERCE AND JAMES BUCHANAN

Franklin Pierce, a handsome New Hampshire lawyer and politician, was not well known when he was elected president. If he seemed unhappy at times, people remembered that all three of his sons had died—the last one just before his inauguration.

As president, Pierce tried to get more land for the United States. He was unable to buy Cuba from Spain or take over Hawaii. However, in 1853, Pierce made the Gadsden Purchase, buying land from Mexico that today forms the southern part of Arizona and New Mexico.

Pierce felt that each new state should decide for itself whether or not to have slavery. He signed the Kansas-Nebraska Act, overriding the 1820 Missouri Compromise, which outlawed slavery in the Northern part of the nation. When it became clear that the settlers in Kansas would decide whether or not to allow slavery in the new state, people on both sides of the issue rushed in. Violence resulted and the territory was nicknamed "Bleeding Kansas."

The Democratic Party did not want to nominate Pierce again. They chose James Buchanan, who had not been involved in the Kansas-Nebraska Act or its violent aftermath. Buchanan was afraid the Southern states would leave the Union, so he tried to keep both sides satisfied. He supported the Supreme Court's decision in the Dred Scott case, which said that slaves and their descendants had no rights and suggested that the federal government could not stop any state or territory from having slavery. Many Americans were furious at the decision. Then Buchanan split his own party by asking Congress to accept Kansas as a slave state. Congress did not accept that plan, and Kansas remained a territory.

Buchanan is the only U.S. president who never married. His niece, Harriet Lane, acted as hostess while Buchanan was in the White House. Buchanan was not nominated by his party again. In 1860, Abraham Lincoln, of the antislavery Republican Party, was elected. In the last months of Buchanan's term, before Lincoln took office, states began to secede from the Union.

Across

2. Lincoln belonged to this political party, which opposed slavery.
4. Buchanan asked Congress to accept Kansas as this kind of state.
8. Both Pierce and Buchanan belonged to this political party.
10. Two-letter abbreviation of Pierce's home state
11. Pierce was the first president to celebrate this holiday with a tree in the White House.
12. Pierce's purchase of land in the Southwest was called the _____ Purchase.
13. People rushed into this territory to decide if it would be a free or slave state.
14. Buchanan sided with the decision in the Dred _____ case.
15. Buchanan's relative who was hostess in the White House

Pierce was the first president to have a Christmas tree in the White House.

Down

1. Land bought in the Gadsden Purchase became part of ____ Mexico.
3. Adjective used to describe the violent Kansas territory
4. Buchanan feared the Southern states would do this.
5. Two-letter abbreviation of a state containing land from the Gadsden Purchase
6. Opposite of begin; Pierce's and Buchanan's presidencies reached this after only one term each
7. The Missouri Compromise of 1820 outlawed slavery in this area of the nation.
9. Adjective describing Pierce's looks
11. Island in the Caribbean that Pierce wanted to acquire
14. Male child; each of Pierce's died

PIERCE
1853–1857

BUCHANAN
1857–1861

Word List

AZ	Cuba	handsome	niece	secede
bleeding	Democratic	Kansas	Northern	slave
Christmas	end	New	Republican	son
	Gadsden	NH	Scott	

ABRAHAM LINCOLN

Abe Lincoln was born in a Kentucky log cabin and grew up on the frontier in Indiana and Illinois. Young Abe loved to read and often borrowed books that he read at night by firelight.

As a young man, Lincoln studied law on his own. He married Mary Todd, a woman some people believe had a bad temper, in 1842. He was elected to the Illinois state legislature, and then to the House of Representatives. He argued that slavery should not be allowed in new territories, although it was acceptable in the existing ones. When Lincoln ran for the U.S. Senate, he challenged his rival, Democrat Stephen A. Douglas, to a series of debates. Although he lost the election, the Lincoln-Douglas debates made Lincoln famous. People appreciated his homespun wit and wisdom. Two years later, he was elected president. Lincoln, and the antislavery Republican Party, wanted to preserve the Union, but the Southern states had already started to secede. Soon after Lincoln took office, Southerners fired on federal troops at Fort Sumter, South Carolina, and the Civil War began.

Lincoln faced enormous challenges as president during this time. The war became long and drawn out. On January 1, 1863, Lincoln issued the Emancipation Proclamation, freeing the slaves in the rebelling states. Lincoln worried greatly about the suffering of the nation's people during the war. During his famous Gettysburg Address in Pennsylvania, Lincoln asked Americans to continue fighting for freedom and democracy so that the soldiers would not have died in vain. Lincoln walked the streets of the capital and the halls of the War Department late at night, grieving and thinking. After trying many other generals, Lincoln finally put Ulysses S. Grant in charge of the Union army.

Lincoln was reelected as the war drew to an end. He urged Congress to restore the nation as soon as rebel states promised their loyalty. "Blood cannot restore blood," he said, "and government should not act for revenge." Lincoln's plans for the future were cut short. He was shot at Ford's Theater in Washington, D.C., by John Wilkes Booth, a bitter Southerner seeking his own revenge.

Across

1. Congressman Lincoln was known for opposing slavery in these places.
5. Last name of the person with whom Lincoln debated when he ran for Senate
9. Lincoln's _____ Proclamation declared an end to slavery in the Confederate states.
10. Kind of animal Jack, a pet in the Lincoln household, was
11. Lincoln's profession before he entered politics
12. The kind of city Washington, D.C., is; where Lincoln walked the streets worrying
15. Lincoln said, "Blood cannot restore _____."
16. Lincoln was a member of this before he ran for the Senate.
17. Lincoln died from a gun____ wound.

Down

1. Lincoln's wife's maiden name
2. Kind of building; where Lincoln was assassinated
3. Last state Lincoln lived in before he became president
4. The Lincoln-Douglas debates were part of a campaign for this kind of seat.
6. Lincoln tried out several of these before he settled on Grant.
7. Kind of hat in which Lincoln sometimes stored papers
8. Pennsylvania battleground where Lincoln gave a famous address
13. Sumter was a federal ____.
14. Last name of Lincoln's assassin

LINCOLN 1861–1865

Lincoln, shown here in his famous stovepipe hat, kept a pet turkey named Jack. The bird had been rescued from becoming a Thanksgiving dinner.

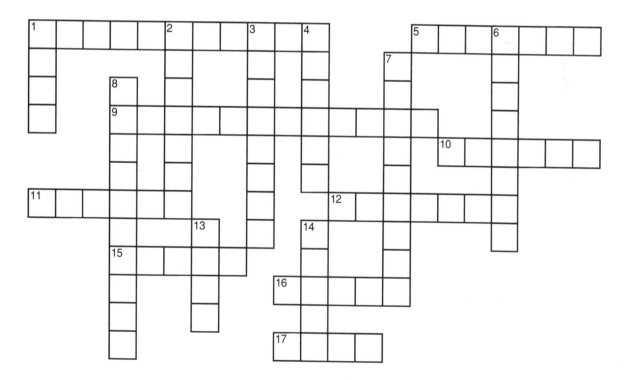

Word List

blood	Douglas	Gettysburg	Senate	theater
Booth	Emancipation	House	shot	Todd
capital	fort	Illinois	stovepipe	turkey
	generals	lawyer	territories	

ANDREW JOHNSON AND ULYSSES S. GRANT

Andrew Johnson and Ulysses S. Grant, two very different presidents, oversaw the aftermath of the Civil War.

Johnson grew up without schooling in North Carolina. His sixteen-year-old bride helped him learn to write. A strong speaker, he took various government positions, from city council to the U.S. Senate. During the Civil War, he was the only Southerner who did not leave the Senate. He explained that he was against Lincoln, "but still I love my country." For Lincoln's second term, the Republican Party invited Johnson to run as his vice president, creating a "unity" ticket between the North and the South.

As president, Johnson wanted to follow Lincoln's ideas for a lenient Reconstruction program, treating the former rebel states kindly while rebuilding after the war. Radical Republicans in Congress favored harsher treatment. They became angry after Johnson vetoed several of their bills, and they tried to get rid of him. He was impeached (formally accused of a crime) for dismissing his secretary of war without the Senate's permission. The Senate was one vote short of finding Johnson guilty. Then, in 1867, the Republicans gained a two-thirds majority in Congress, which meant they could overturn Johnson's vetoes. Congress and the army took control of Reconstruction of the South.

In the next presidential election, General Ulysses S. Grant, a hero of the Civil War, was elected. Grant, the son of Jesse and Hannah Simpson Grant, was originally named Hiram Ulysses, but his family called him Ulysses or 'Lyss. He decided to adopt the name Ulysses S. Grant after a clerical error was made listing his name as Ulysses Simpson at West Point. Grant was certainly at his best as a general. Lincoln once said of him, "I can't spare this man. He fights." As president, though, Grant did not do as well. He had no political experience before taking office. Reconstruction of the South did not go smoothly. White Southerners resented Reconstruction, and secret groups such as the Ku Klux Klan terrorized African Americans. Although Grant was an honest man, his administration was marked by one scandal after another. Grant decided not to run for a third term.

Across

1. Initials of Johnson's job under Lincoln
4. Federal program intended to rebuild the South after the Civil War
6. Johnson was impeached (but not convicted) for dismissing the secretary of this department without Congress's permission.
8. Number of votes by which Johnson was found not guilty in his impeachment trial
9. Grant was popular as a war ____.
11. Grant's presidency was mired in these, which gave him a bad name.
14. Speech-maker; Johnson was a good one

15. Name for Republicans who wanted major changes in the South after the Civil War
16. Lincoln said of Grant, "I can't spare this man. He _____."

JOHNSON
1865–1869

Down

1. Johnson used this to stop the radical Republicans.
2. Johnson's wife helped teach him to do this.
3. Johnson did not go to _____.
5. Johnson grew up in North _____.
7. Kind of book Grant wrote
10. To formally accuse a president of a crime
11. After impeachment charges were made, Johnson was tried by this group.
12. Johnson was opposed to Lincoln but still had this for his country.
13. Kind of ticket created with Northerner Lincoln for president and Southerner Johnson for vice president

Grant finished writing his memoirs a month before he died.

GRANT
1869–1877

Word List

Carolina	impeach	radical	Senate	VP
fights	love	Reconstruction	speaker	war
hero	memoirs	scandals	unity	write
	one	school	veto	

RUTHERFORD B. HAYES, JAMES A. GARFIELD, AND CHESTER A. ARTHUR

Rutherford B. Hayes almost did not become president. He lost the vote of the electors (the representatives who elect the president) to Democratic candidate Samuel J. Tilden. However, the Republican Party challenged the voting results in three Southern states, as well as Oregon. The decision might have resulted in a deadlock if it had gone to Congress, which was made up of a Democratic House and a Republican Senate, but the Republicans and Democrats struck a deal. The questionable votes would go to Hayes, making him president, but he would have to pull the army troops out of the South and end Reconstruction. That is how Hayes became president. In the South, white Democrats took control and received little interference from the federal government for a long time.

Hayes entered the presidency with a solid reputation. He had been a Civil War general and governor of Ohio. Hayes and his wife, nicknamed "Lemonade Lucy" because she banned alcohol in the White House, were religious and honest. Hayes made every effort to live by his motto: "He serves his party best who serves his country best."

Like Hayes, James A. Garfield was a Republican from Ohio and an officer in the Civil War. He served seventeen years in Congress before he was elected president. Garfield was the first president to be fluent in Spanish. His vice president, Chester Arthur, was from a Republican group called the "Stalwarts." Garfield had been president for less than seven months when he was assassinated. He was shot by a mentally disturbed man named Charles J. Guiteau, who cried, "I am a Stalwart; now Arthur is president!" Although it was later shown that Guiteau was not acting as part of a conspiracy for the Stalwarts, Chester Arthur entered the presidency with a cloud over his head. Some people thought the Stalwarts would stop at nothing to get what they wanted.

Arthur was opposed to reform, but he did back a new civil service law, changing the way people got federal government jobs. He also improved the navy and the postal system. He had such a large wardrobe—including eighty pairs of pants!—that people called him "Elegant Arthur."

Across

1. Republican group of which Arthur was a member
4. The U.S. _____ system was improved by Arthur.
5. First word of Arthur's nickname
8. Improvement; what Arthur finally did for the civil service
12. Forthright; Hayes was thought to be this
13. Stop; Reconstruction came to an ___ under Hayes
14. Office Hayes held in Ohio

16. Garfield served seventeen years in this.
17. First word of nickname for Hayes's wife

Down

1. Garfield was fluent in this language.
2. Garfield's assassin _____ him with a gun.
3. Arthur improved this fighting force.
6. Arthur helped reform this kind of job.
7. Garfield was killed in the seventh _____ of his presidency.
9. These representatives elected someone else, but the Republicans said Hayes should have won.
10. The civil _____ is the system of government jobs.
11. Arthur had eighty pairs of these.
15. As part of his election agreement, Hayes had to pull this force out of the South.

HAYES
1877–1881

GARFIELD
1881

ARTHUR
1881–1885

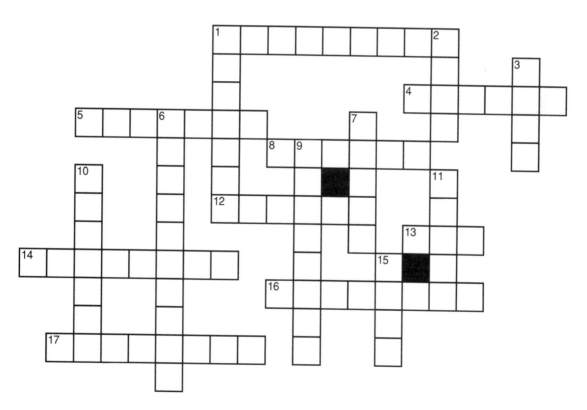

Word List

army	Elegant	honest	pants	shot
Congress	end	Lemonade	postal	Spanish
electors	government	month	reform	Stalwarts
	governor	navy	service	

27

GROVER CLEVELAND

At the end of Grover Cleveland's first term, his wife told the White House servants to take care of things while she and her husband were gone. They'd be sure to return, she said, in four years! It turned out to be true—Grover Cleveland was the only president to serve a term, be out a term, and then serve a second term.

Cleveland was known as an honest reformer. He cleaned up government as Buffalo's mayor, then as governor of New York. In 1884, Cleveland ran for president as a Democrat, receiving extra support from a reform-minded group of Republicans called the "mugwumps."

In office, Cleveland enforced the Pendleton Civil Service Act, which had been signed by President Arthur. Thousands of jobs once given out as political favors were made available to the public. Cleveland made the railroads give back land they had claimed illegally. He vetoed bills that would have given pensions to Civil War veterans who had not been wounded. Cleveland wanted a low tariff, but he was unable to achieve this.

In 1888, Cleveland ran for reelection against Benjamin Harrison. It was a tight race, but Cleveland lost. Four years later, Cleveland rode a large vote into office again, defeating Harrison this time. Soon afterward, the panic of 1893 led to a major economic depression. Cleveland tried to change the U.S. treasury system but was unable to improve the situation and received a lot of the blame for the country's economic troubles. Earlier, in 1892, Cleveland sent federal troops to end the Pullman railroad strike in Chicago. Although that move was favored by businesses, it angered union workers.

Although Cleveland was not always popular, his oldest daughter, Ruth, was so well liked that she had a candy bar named after her. Baby Ruth bars are still sold in stores today.

Across

3. City where Cleveland was mayor
5. Cleveland made the railroads give some of this back to the nation.
7. Cleveland enforced the civil service law this president had signed.
9. Group of Republicans who supported Cleveland
11. Economic problem during Cleveland's second term
13. Workers' organizations that disliked Cleveland when he stopped a strike
15. Grover and Frances Cleveland had their _____ in the White House.
17. City where Cleveland sent troops to end the Pullman strike
18. Government money system, which Cleveland tried to change in order to end the depression

Down

1. Opposite of high; kind of tariff Cleveland wanted
2. Railroad sleeping car; makers of this car went on strike
4. Number of years between Cleveland's terms as president
6. Cleveland wanted a low one.

8. Last name of president who held office between Cleveland's terms
10. Government payments that support veterans; Cleveland did not allow fit men to have them
12. Opposite of begin; though defeated after one term, Cleveland's presidency had not come to this
14. Initials of the state where Cleveland was governor
16. The _____ Ruth candy bar was named after Cleveland's daughter.

CLEVELAND
1885–1889
and
1893–1897

An illustration of Cleveland's White House wedding to his much younger wife, Frances

Word List				
Arthur	Chicago	Harrison	NY	treasury
Baby	depression	land	pensions	unions
Buffalo	end	low	Pullman	wedding
	four	mugwumps	tariff	

BENJAMIN HARRISON AND WILLIAM McKINLEY

Benjamin Harrison was an Indiana lawyer, an officer in the Civil War, and a senator. When he ran against Cleveland for president, he got votes largely because his name was so well known. His grandfather, William Henry Harrison, had been president many years earlier. Harrison also had the backing of business leaders who wanted a high tariff, or tax on imported goods. Harrison signed the McKinley Tariff Act, written by House member and future president William McKinley. The new tariff raised prices and increased profits for U.S. manufacturers. People with less money, such as farmers, laborers, and especially America's flood of new immigrants, were unhappy with the high prices. They also wanted better wages and working conditions. At the end of Harrison's term, President Cleveland returned to office.

Although McKinley supported a high tariff, he was voted into office because the economy had worsened during Cleveland's second term. McKinley had been a lawyer, a congressman, and governor of Ohio. As a presidential candidate, McKinley received support from the powerful business and financial leaders in the Republican Party, who feared his opponent, William Jennings Bryan, would upset the economy by changing the basis of U.S. money from gold to silver.

McKinley's first term was marked by the Spanish-American War. American newspapers published sensational stories about Cuba's fight for independence from Spain, urging the United States to help free Cuba. This "yellow journalism" was only partly true, but it convinced many people that the United States should act. After the United States became involved in the Spanish-American War, Cuba won its independence, and the United States gained control of the Philippines, Puerto Rico, and Guam. McKinley later accepted Hawaii as a U.S. territory and divided the Samoan Islands with Germany. Only seven months into his second term, McKinley was assassinated by Leon Czolgosz, an anarchist who was disturbed by social injustice.

Across

2. Last name of presidential candidate who wanted to change the basis of U.S. money
5. The United States divided the Samoan Islands with this country.
7. The United States helped this island country win its independence from Spain.
8. Not a colony; describes Cuba, as a result of the Spanish-American War
10. McKinley's home state
13. Person who rebels against governmental authority; McKinley's assassin was one
14. This island became a U.S. territory after the Spanish-American War: Puerto _____.
15. First word in Harrison's nickname
16. Bryan wanted to base the American currency on this precious metal.

Down

Harrison's nickname was "Little Ben."

1. Harrison's relative who had been president
3. Color used to represent shoddy, or sensationalist, journalism
4. Metal basis of U.S. money that McKinley wanted to keep
5. Small Pacific island of which the United States gained control after the Spanish-American War
6. Last name of the president who took office after Cleveland's second term
8. Harrison's home state
9. Gains for business owners; Harrison's high tariff increased these for U.S. manufacturers
11. This territory of islands, gained during McKinley's presidency, eventually became a state.
12. What things cost; affected by a high tariff

HARRISON 1889–1893

McKINLEY 1897–1901

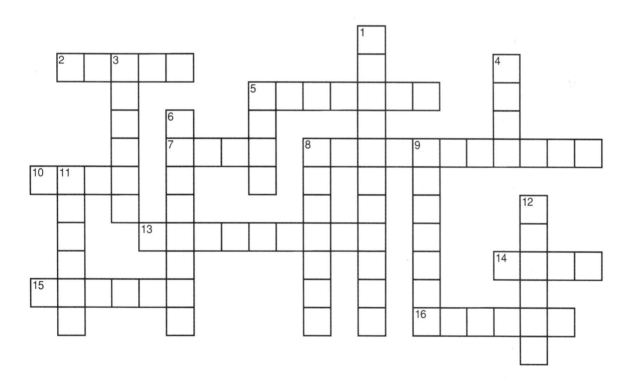

Word List

anarchist	Germany	Hawaii	McKinley	Rico
Bryan	gold	independent	Ohio	silver
Cuba	grandfather	Indiana	prices	yellow
	Guam	Little	profits	

THEODORE ROOSEVELT

As a child, Theodore Roosevelt was so sick with asthma and other illnesses that he had to be tutored at home instead of going to school. When he was thirteen, he began an exercise program and eventually became strong and energetic. His enthusiasm for fresh air and exercise lasted the rest of his life.

Born well-off, Roosevelt went to Harvard University, then held a number of government positions. He worked as a rancher in the Dakota Territory for two years after his mother and his first wife died. He worked in President McKinley's administration during the Spanish-American War before deciding to join the fight himself. After the war, Roosevelt was elected governor of New York.

Roosevelt became vice president during McKinley's second term. He was made president when McKinley was assassinated in 1901. Roosevelt was just forty-two years old at the time, making him the youngest president in U.S. history.

During his two terms as president, Roosevelt accomplished a lot. He believed people should have a fair, or "square," deal. He tried to break up large business groups that controlled prices, called "trusts." He also managed to raise wages for coal miners. He supported the Pure Food and Drug Act and the Meat Inspection Act, raising standards for food and medicine. He received the Nobel Peace Prize for his role as mediator in the Russo-Japanese War. He built up the navy and encouraged the building of the Panama Canal on the isthmus of Panama. Roosevelt said it was best to "speak softly and carry a big stick."

Roosevelt also supported the creation of many national parks and forests. Once, while on a hunting trip, Roosevelt refused to shoot a bear cub. A toy maker created the first "Teddy Bear" in honor of Roosevelt.

The White House was a lively place while Roosevelt was in office. He always made time to play with his six adventurous and fun-loving children.

Across

4. Roosevelt worked for laws that would preserve the wilderness in national parks and _____.
5. Term for the kind of deal Roosevelt promised voters
6. Medicines; Roosevelt wanted federal standards for these and for food
9. Healthy activity that Roosevelt favored
11. Roosevelt fought in the _____-American War.
13. Some players of this game were members of the Rough Riders.
14. Narrow land between bodies of water; the Panama Canal was built across one
16. Roosevelt's home state: New _____
17. Territory where Roosevelt ranched for two years

Down

1. Large business combinations that Roosevelt tried to break up
2. Roosevelt was elected to this position after the Spanish-American War.

3. Stuffed animal named after Roosevelt
7. Number of children Roosevelt had
8. Health problem Roosevelt experienced as a child
10. Roosevelt said, "Speak softly and carry a big _____."
12. Roosevelt built up this fighting force.
13. Without impurities; the ideal state of food and drugs
15. First word in the name of the hill the Rough Riders charged up in Cuba

Theodore Roosevelt with the Rough Riders at the top of San Juan Hill in Cuba during the Spanish-American War. Roosevelt formed the cavalry regiment with friends, including cowboys from the west and polo players from the east.

**ROOSEVELT
1901–1909**

Word List

asthma	drugs	isthmus	San	stick
bear	exercise	navy	six	trusts
Dakota	forests	polo	Spanish	York
	governor	pure	square	

WILLIAM H. TAFT

William H. Taft grew up in Cincinnati, Ohio. His family called him "Big Lug" because of his size—he was six feet tall and weighed as much as 330 pounds. However, Taft was athletic. He liked to play tennis and dance, and even learned to surf in Waikiki.

Taft was an Ohio state court judge before he became governor of the Philippines, which were recently gained through the Spanish-American War. Taft improved conditions all around and gave the people of the Philippines limited self-government. In 1904, he returned to the United States to become President Roosevelt's secretary of war. Roosevelt wanted Taft to succeed him as president when he retired, and Taft easily won the election.

Soon after taking office, Taft found out that being president was difficult and often "lonesome." Many people, including Theodore Roosevelt, thought Taft acted too conservatively, but he did his best to carry out the policies Roosevelt had set in place. Taft's administration attempted to break up ninety trusts, or business combinations, which was even more than Roosevelt had targeted while president. Taft supported the establishment of a federal income tax, which was charged according to the amount a person earned.

Taft favored "dollar diplomacy," which meant using trade and investments to influence other countries. He even sent troops to Central America to protect American property and lives. Some people believed that the U.S. Army was under the control of American business.

The Republicans nominated Taft for a second term. Theodore Roosevelt, unhappy with the job Taft was doing, decided to run for president again and formed his own political party to do so. As a result, the Republican vote was split and the election went to the Democratic candidate, Woodrow Wilson.

Taft was glad to leave the White House. He was later appointed chief justice of the Supreme Court, a job he had wanted all his life.

Across

3. Taft became chief _____ of the Supreme Court.
5. Racquet sport that Taft enjoyed
9. Taft acted as governor of these islands.
10. Taft favored this kind of tax.
12. Nickname for Taft's diplomacy based on monetary incentives
13. Taft had to have an extra-large one put in the White House.
14. Last name of the Democrat who defeated Taft after one term
15. Court Taft last worked in
16. Initials of the president under whom Taft was vice president

Down

1. Taft learned to do this in Waikiki.
2. Taft's home city
4. Taft's description of the presidency
6. Number of business trusts Taft's administration tried to break up
7. Taft gave the people of the Philippines limited ____-government.
8. Taft sent troops to this part of the Americas.
11. Taft's job before he became governor of the Philippines
14. Violent conflict between nations; led the United States to acquire the Philippines

TAFT
1909–1913

Taft, who was a big man, had an extra-large tub installed in the White House.

Word List

bathtub	dollar	lonesome	Supreme	war
Central	income	ninety	surf	Wilson
Cincinnati	judge	Philippines	tennis	
	justice	self	TR	

WOODROW WILSON

Woodrow Wilson was one of the most learned presidents. He was a professor at and president of Princeton University before he was elected governor of New Jersey. Just two years later, he became president, largely because the opposing vote was split between Theodore Roosevelt and William Taft.

Wilson felt that Congress represented special regions and interests but the president should "look out for the general interests of the whole country." He worked for a lower tariff, or tax on imported goods, which angered some manufacturers but lowered prices for most Americans. He established the Federal Reserve System to regulate the nation's banks and money supply. He supported laws that would improve conditions for workers, including one that restricted railroad workers to eight-hour workdays.

Wilson is most famous for his role as a leader in World War I. He tried hard to keep the nation out of the war, until German submarines began attacking American ships. Once the United States entered the war, the tide turned against Germany. Wilson named the "Fourteen Points" he thought were needed to create a lasting peace once the war was over. The most important one was the formation of the League of Nations, where countries could meet to resolve disputes instead of going to war. In 1918, Wilson met with other world leaders in Versailles, France, to create a treaty to end the war. The Treaty of Versailles contained some of the points Wilson had proposed, but he was forced to compromise on several issues.

At home, though, Wilson could not get the Senate to agree to the treaty. They were afraid the League of Nations would reduce the power of the United States. Wilson became ill during a trip to rally public support for the treaty. Soon afterward, he suffered a stroke and did not appear publicly for months. His wife, Edith, took messages to him and announced his decisions. Some historians believe that Edith may actually have been making the decisions herself. The treaty was never approved by the Senate.

Across

2. Number of hours railroad workers could work each day under Wilson's law
6. Wilson first worked at Princeton as a _____.
7. When Wilson won the presidency, the opposition vote was split between Roosevelt and ____.
10. Attacks by these German boats on American ships caused the United States to enter World War I.
12. Wilson's ____ helped manage the presidency after he had a stroke.
14. Some people believe that Edith Wilson temporarily acted as _____.
15. Wilson proposed an international organization, called the _____ of Nations.
16. Number of the world war that occurred while Wilson was president
17. Animals Wilson had grazing on the White House lawn

Down

1. Event that kept Wilson out of public view for months
3. Enemy of the United States during World War I

4. These were split three ways when Wilson won the presidency.
5. Location in France where the treaty that ended World War I was written
6. Wilson was president of this university.
8. Number of points in Wilson's World War I peace plan
9. Amounts things cost; these are lower with a low tariff
11. This U.S. government body would not approve the Treaty of Versailles.
13. Wilson was governor of ____ Jersey.

**WILSON
1913–1921**

*During World War I, President Wilson used sheep to mow the
White House lawn instead of men who could help the war effort.*

Word List

eight	League	prices	sheep	Versailles
fourteen	New	Princeton	stroke	votes
Germany	one	professor	submarines	wife
	president	Senate	Taft	

WARREN G. HARDING AND CALVIN COOLIDGE

Warren G. Harding and Calvin Coolidge, two very different men, took office as president and vice president in 1921. Harding was tall, handsome, and likable, but he had spent most of his time as a senator doing favors for friends back home in Ohio. Coolidge was a strict, conservative New Englander. He became famous when, as governor of Massachusetts, he broke up a Boston police strike by calling in the National Guard. "There is no right to strike against the public safety," he declared, "by anyone, anywhere, any time."

Harding probably won the presidency because he promised a return to "normalcy" after World War I. He was opposed to the League of Nations, but he called for the Washington Disarmament Conference. There, the United States and other nations agreed to reduce the size of their navies.

Harding preferred gambling, drinking, and playing golf to work. He gave friends from Ohio jobs in Washington, D.C. Many of them were without ability; others were careless of their duties. The press called them the "Ohio Gang." Three years into his term, Harding died suddenly, probably from a heart attack. After Harding's death, many scandals became known publicly, including the Teapot Dome scandal in which the secretary of the interior was found guilty of accepting over $3 million in bribes to rent government land to oil drillers.

Calvin Coolidge was an honest president. He made government more efficient and economical. He did not believe government should interfere in private business, even though people seemed to be gambling on the stock market. "The business of America is business," he declared. Coolidge served the remainder of Harding's term plus one of his own. He retired a few months before the stock market crashed in 1929, leading to the worst economic depression in U.S. history.

Across

3. Harding probably died of a heart _____.
6. Leaders agreed to reduce the size of these at the Washington Disarmament Conference.
8. Where Coolidge was governor
10. Sport Harding played during work hours
11. Two-letter abbreviation of Harding's home state
12. Coolidge was called "____ Cal."
13. Coolidge did not interfere when people appeared to be gambling on this market.
14. What Harding wanted to return to after World War I
17. Coolidge was famous for breaking up one in Boston.

Coolidge spoke so little he was called "Silent Cal."

Down

1. Harding's political friends were called the "Ohio ____."
2. Description of Harding's looks
4. First word in the name of a scandal from Harding's presidency
5. Setting aside arms; purpose of a major conference during Harding's administration
6. While governor, Coolidge broke up a police strike by calling in the _____ Guard.
7. Coolidge said that no one had a right to strike against the public _____.
9. What Coolidge said the business of America is
15. Second word of Coolidge's nickname
16. Harding's secretary of the interior accepted bribes from drillers of this.

HARDING
1921–1923

COOLIDGE
1923–1929

Word List

attack	disarmament	Massachusetts	OH	stock
business	Gang	National	oil	strike
Cal	golf	navies	safety	Teapot
	handsome	normalcy	Silent	

HERBERT HOOVER

Herbert Hoover was perhaps most remarkable for all the things he did when he was not president. By profession, he was a mining engineer, educated in the first class at Stanford University in California. As a young man, he managed mines all over the world and became very wealthy. Hoover was living in London when World War I began, and he organized a committee to help his fellow Americans get home from Europe. Soon he was heading the Commission for Relief in Belgium, which helped distribute aid in war-torn Europe.

President Wilson took advantage of Hoover's experience, making him the wartime U.S. food administrator, responsible for getting Americans to save food so more would be available for the troops. Then, after World War I, Hoover headed a council to distribute food to the hungry in Europe.

By this time, Hoover was so well known that President Harding named him secretary of commerce. He did so much for the country that people called him "Undersecretary of Everything Else." Hoover was untouched by the scandals of Harding's administration.

In 1928, Hoover was elected president—his first elective office. Just seven months into his presidency, the Great Depression struck. About a quarter of all Americans were out of work; many were homeless and hungry. Hoover increased government loans to banks and businesses and supported some public works projects, but he did not think it was right for the government to give aid to poor people or create jobs with borrowed money. He was afraid that would destroy the individual American's drive to succeed. Although he had not created the conditions that led to the economic troubles, Hoover was blamed for the depression. At the end of his term, he was defeated by a landslide.

Hoover continued to help others after he left office. In 1946, President Truman made Hoover chairman of the Famine Emergency Commission in Europe. He later worked on two different commissions to help make government more efficient.

Across

4. Hoover was secretary of this department under Harding.
5. Voted into office; for Hoover, the first time was the presidency
7. Hoover headed Belgium's Commission for _____.
9. Word used for camps of the poor and unemployed during the depression
10. Term for a big election win
11. Mass hunger; Hoover helped fight this in Europe
13. Hoover trained for this profession at Stanford.
15. Money to be repaid; Hoover preferred this to a handout
16. University Hoover attended

Down

1. Fraction of Americans out of work in the Great Depression: one- _____.
2. Opposite of poor; what Hoover was

3. As secretary of commerce, Hoover was called "_____ of Everything Else."
6. The last commissions Hoover served on were supposed to make government more _____.
8. Edible items; during World War I, Hoover was administrator of this for the nation

10. British city where Hoover lived for a time
12. As a young man, Hoover managed these.
14. Help; given out by many Hoover-led groups
17. Number of terms Hoover served

HOOVER 1929–1933

The tent and shack cities of the unemployed during the Great Depression were called "Hoovervilles."

Word List

aid	elected	fourth	London	Stanford
commerce	engineer	Hoovervilles	mines	Undersecretary
efficient	famine	landslide	one	wealthy
	food	loan	Relief	

FRANKLIN DELANO ROOSEVELT

Franklin Delano Roosevelt, often called "FDR," was born into a wealthy and well-connected family. In fact, he was related to eleven former American presidents. He was also distantly related to the woman he married. Trained in the law, FDR served in the New York State Senate before President Wilson made him assistant secretary of the navy.

At age 39, FDR contracted polio, which left his legs paralyzed. For the rest of his life, he wore leg braces and used crutches or a wheelchair. He ran for governor of New York in 1928. When the Great Depression struck, he took measures to help suffering people in his state.

The Democrats nominated Roosevelt for president in 1932. He offered Americans the New Deal, promising that the government would do much more to relieve suffering and end the depression. In the so-called "First Hundred Days" of his presidency, FDR put through a storm of new laws. He temporarily closed banks to end panic withdrawals, then reopened them with federal help and deposit insurance. Later, he fought for laws that lay a foundation of security for Americans, creating Social Security, unemployment insurance, and federal aid to dependent children. FDR's radio talks, called "fireside chats," gave people new confidence. "The only thing we have to fear is fear itself," Roosevelt said.

FDR would have done even more to control business and industry, but the Supreme Court blocked some of his measures. In 1937, he tried to enlarge the size of the Court in order to appoint judges who would agree with him, but the plan failed.

The nation appreciated FDR's strong leadership during World War II. He died at the start of his last term, in 1945. Roosevelt was elected to four terms—no other president had been elected to more than two terms! Congress later passed a law limiting presidents to two consecutive terms in office.

Across

3. First word of the state in which Roosevelt was senator
7. Disease Roosevelt contracted
8. Court Roosevelt unsuccessfully tried to enlarge
10. Young people; Roosevelt began a program of federal aid for dependent ones
11. Eleanor Roosevelt helped create the Universal Declaration of _____ Rights.
13. Roosevelt worked as assistant _____ of the navy.
14. Term used for Roosevelt's radio chats
15. Roosevelt generally needed this to walk.
16. Eleanor worked for equality without regard to this.

Down

1. Roosevelt proposed this kind of insurance.
2. Maximum number of terms for which any president had been elected before Roosevelt

4. Number of presidents to whom Roosevelt was related
5. Initials by which Roosevelt is known
6. First name of Roosevelt's wife
8. Social _____ was begun by Roosevelt.
9. Number of days at the start of his presidency when Roosevelt accomplished a lot
12. Roosevelt said, "The only thing we have to fear is _____ itself."
14. Number of terms for which Roosevelt was elected

ROOSEVELT
1933–1945

Eleanor Roosevelt, one of the greatest first ladies, worked hard to achieve equality for people of all races and wrote the Universal Declaration of Human Rights.

Word List

children	eleven	four	polio	Supreme
crutch	FDR	Human	race	two
Eleanor	fear	hundred	secretary	unemployment
	fireside	New	Security	

HARRY S. TRUMAN

Harry S. Truman had served only eighty-two days as vice president when Franklin Roosevelt's death pushed him into the presidency. As a young man, Truman was not able to afford to go to college, but he had read every book in the Independence, Missouri, library by the time he was fifteen. He entered politics as a county official, then was elected senator. Roosevelt chose Truman to be his running mate for 1944 because his last vice president was seen to be too liberal.

Truman proved to be an energetic president who did not hesitate to attack his critics. In his first term, Truman tried to pass new civil rights laws and expand Social Security, but Congress refused to cooperate. Truman's greatest challenges came from abroad, however. World War II came to an end in Europe soon after he took office, but the war continued in the Pacific. Truman decided to use the newly developed atomic bomb on the Japanese. It is estimated that more than 130,000 people were killed in the atomic explosions at Hiroshima and Nagasaki. Historians still argue over whether or not the bombing was needed to end the war and therefore save lives that might have been lost in an invasion of Japan.

At the end of the war, Truman put through the Marshall Plan, a vast aid program for Europe. He also came to Berlin's aid when the Soviets threatened to take control of it in 1948. With roads closed, he ordered planes to carry supplies to the parts of the city that were controlled by the United States and its allies. The airlift succeeded, and the Soviets opened the city again.

During his second term, Truman focused much of his attention on the Korean War. In 1950, communist North Korea invaded South Korea. Truman sent U.S. troops to Korea, then asked for backing from the United Nations, an international organization that had been formed in 1945. Truman was very concerned about stopping the spread of communism.

Truman's wife and daughter were so much a part of his life that White House staff called them "the Three Musketeers." His wife, Bess, often gave him valued advice, and Truman called her "the Boss."

Across

1. Name of the vast aid plan Truman approved for postwar Europe
3. Truman's nickname for his wife
6. People who find fault; Truman attacked his
9. Initials of the organization that entered the Korean War at Truman's request
10. White House staff used this nickname for the Trumans: the Three _____.
11. Truman approved this type of program, supplying Berlin by plane
13. North Korea had this political system.
15. Female child; Truman had one
16. Truman played it expertly.

Down

1. Two-letter abbreviation of Truman's home state
2. One of the Japanese cities hit by an atomic bomb
4. Truman was one when he was chosen to be vice president.
5. Truman came to the aid of _____ Korea.
7. Congress blocked Truman's proposals for new laws guaranteeing this kind of rights.

**TRUMAN
1945–1953**

Truman, an expert pianist, playing the piano he was presented with at the White House

8. Truman approved the use of this new, very deadly kind of bomb.
12. As a boy, Truman read every book in this place.
13. Truman entered politics at this government level.
14. First word in title of Truman's job before he became president

Word List

airlift	civil	daughter	MO	South
atomic	communist	Hiroshima	Musketeers	UN
Boss	county	library	piano	vice
	critics	Marshall	senator	

DWIGHT D. EISENHOWER

"I like Ike!" was Dwight D. Eisenhower's campaign slogan, and it was what people said about him all his life.

Eisenhower grew up in Abilene, Kansas. He attended West Point military academy and became a career officer. At the beginning of World War II, he was asked to command the War Plans Division of the War Department. His global strategy and early plan for the invasion of France were so good that President Roosevelt put him in charge of the U.S. Army in Europe. Soon he was heading the Allied forces there, coordinating armies and officers from six different countries. By the end of the war, Eisenhower, who had many good ideas and got along well with people, was an international hero. Both political parties wanted him to be their presidential candidate, but he didn't commit until 1952, when he decided to run as a Republican.

Eisenhower declared that he had already taken part in war and, as president, wanted to make peace. After his inauguration, Eisenhower helped arrange a peace agreement between North and South Korea, ending the Korean War. Like Truman, Eisenhower worried about communism spreading to more countries. He put forth the Eisenhower Doctrine, which said that any country in the Middle East threatened by communists could ask for U.S. aid. He sent troops to Lebanon when they were requested. Eisenhower also tried to deal directly with Soviet communist leaders in summit talks, although these stopped for a time when an American U-2 spy plane was shot down over the Soviet Union.

At home, in a time of prosperity, Eisenhower did little to change the policies set by Presidents Roosevelt and Truman. He enforced existing civil rights laws, sending federal troops to make sure African American students could attend school in Little Rock, Arkansas, in 1957. He helped initiate the interstate highway system. And Eisenhower warned the nation that American arms-makers were combining with the armed forces in a "military-industrial complex" that was dangerous and expensive for the nation.

Across

1. Eisenhower's nickname
2. Schemes or ideas for the future; Eisenhower made good ones for World War II
5. Eisenhower worried about the spread of this political belief system.
8. Number of terms Eisenhower served
9. Eisenhower's hometown
11. Eisenhower said that, as president, he wanted to make _____.
12. Eisenhower renamed the presidential retreat _____ David after his grandson.
13. In the war, Eisenhower coordinated armies from this number of nations.
14. The Eisenhower _____ said Middle East countries threatened by communism could get U.S. aid.

Down

Eisenhower painting at Camp David, the presidential retreat formerly called "Shangri-La," which he renamed for his grandson David

1. Kind of highway system Eisenhower helped start
2. Second word in the name of the military academy Eisenhower attended
3. Eisenhower met with leaders of the Soviet Union in this kind of meeting.
4. Continent where Eisenhower served as chief of the armed forces
5. Eisenhower warned against the "military-industrial _____."
6. Both political parties wanted Eisenhower to be their _____ after the war.
7. Asian country where Eisenhower helped to make peace
10. Eisenhower sent troops to this Middle Eastern country.
12. Eisenhower sent federal troops to Little Rock to enforce ____ rights laws.

EISENHOWER
1953–1961

Word List				
Abilene	civil	Europe	Lebanon	six
Camp	communism	Ike	peace	summit
candidate	complex	interstate	plans	two
	Doctrine	Korea	Point	

47

JOHN F. KENNEDY

John F. Kennedy started life with many advantages. He was good looking and wealthy. In fact, he was the first president since George Washington to turn down his salary (he donated it to charities instead). He was also from a large, close family. His brothers and sisters helped him throughout his political career. And Kennedy was a talented thinker and writer. His book, *Profiles in Courage*, about courageous senators in history, won a Pulitzer Prize in 1957.

Jack, as he was known to friends and family, went to Harvard, served in the navy during World War II, and became a congressman and then a senator for his home state of Massachusetts. Finally, in 1960, Kennedy was able to achieve his most important goal—the presidency. Kennedy's strong speaking ability helped him win the first televised debates between presidential candidates.

As president, Kennedy started the Peace Corps, which sent American volunteers to serve in poor or underdeveloped countries. His Alliance for Progress was meant to strengthen ties and trade among the nations of the Americas.

In 1961, Kennedy supported an attack on communist Cuba. The Bay of Pigs invasion was an embarrassing failure. The next year, however, Cuba was the scene of a Kennedy policy triumph. Aerial pictures showed that the Soviets were placing missiles in Cuba. President Kennedy told the Soviets to remove the missiles or risk war. After one tense week, Soviet leader Nikita Khrushchev withdrew the missiles. In 1963, tensions eased a little when Kennedy signed a treaty with Britain, France, and the Soviet Union to stop nuclear testing in the atmosphere, underwater, and in outer space.

At home, Kennedy favored strong civil rights laws and worked hard for desegregation in schools. However, it is hard to know what more Kennedy might have accomplished; he was assassinated after only a few years in office. On November 22, 1963, Kennedy was shot during a parade in Dallas, Texas. The alleged assassin, Lee Harvey Oswald, was killed soon afterward, so the public may never know exactly why or how Kennedy was assassinated.

Across

1. Mythic kingdom with which Kennedy's time in office has been compared
5. First name of Kennedy's son
6. Kennedy's nickname
7. City where Kennedy was assassinated
8. First name of Kennedy's daughter
10. Soviet leader during the Cuban missile crisis
13. Kennedy founded the _____ Corps, sending American volunteers to help improve conditions in poor countries.
14. Kind of weapon the Soviets tried to place in Cuba
15. Kennedy gained votes when he debated his rival on ___.
16. State where Kennedy was assassinated

Down

1. Island nation containing the Bay of Pigs
2. Kennedy's home state
3. Kennedy reached an agreement to restrict this.
4. Kennedy _____ his salary to charities.
6. Kennedy's wife's nickname
7. On TV, these helped Kennedy get elected.
9. First word in the title of Kennedy's prizewinning book
11. First name of Kennedy's alleged assassin
12. Name of the bay where Kennedy's failed invasion of Cuba took place

**KENNEDY
1961–1963**

The years Kennedy spent in the White House with Jackie, Caroline, and John Jr. were compared to King Arthur's Camelot, a time of great happiness that was cut short by tragedy.

Word List

Camelot	debates	John	missile	testing
Caroline	donated	Khrushchev	Peace	Texas
Cuba	Jack	Lee	Pigs	TV
Dallas	Jackie	Massachusetts	*Profiles*	

LYNDON B. JOHNSON

Lyndon B. Johnson grew up in Johnson City, a small Texas town named after his grandfather. Johnson's father and both his grandfathers had served in the Texas state legislature. Maybe that is why, when Lyndon was born, his father rode a horse around town shouting that a future U.S. senator had just come into the world.

Johnson taught high school briefly before he entered the House of Representatives and then the Senate. By 1955, he was majority leader (leader of the Democrats) in the Senate. Johnson tried to get his party's presidential nomination in 1960 but agreed to run as vice president when Kennedy was chosen. Johnson became president when Kennedy was assassinated and was easily elected in his own right in 1964.

As Americans mourned Kennedy, Johnson got certain laws through Congress that Kennedy had wanted. He managed to pass several major civil rights laws, including ones protecting the right of African Americans to vote and forbidding employers from discriminating against people on the basis of race or sex. Johnson also got Congress to pass laws to improve housing, provide Medicare for elderly people without health insurance, and protect the environment. He was aiming, he said, for a "Great Society" in which all people would be able to take part and prosper.

However, Johnson's dreams were thwarted. The new civil rights laws did not bring equality and jobs to all poor inner-city African Americans. Frustrations increased and some cities were torn apart by riots. Meanwhile, young men were being drafted to fight in Vietnam. The war there, begun slowly in Eisenhower's day, escalated under Johnson as the United States, with South Vietnam, struggled against communist North Vietnam. Antiwar feelings grew stronger in the United States. In 1968, Johnson shocked the nation by saying he would not run for the presidency again. At the end of his term, he returned to Texas.

Across

5. Johnson's father and grandfathers were all in this Texas government body.
7. Race troubles in cities led to these.
9. Medicare is a form of _____ insurance.
11. Work; Johnson helped guarantee equal opportunity in this
14. Johnson's father rode this around to announce a new senator had been born.
15. Shortened name of the country where the United States was involved in war during Johnson's administration
16. Murder of a president or other important leader
17. Middle name shared by Johnson's wife and one of his daughters
18. These relatives of Johnson were both Texas legislators.

Down

1. Against; Vietnam protesters were ____war
2. Johnson's job before beginning his political career

3. Johnson grew up in Johnson ____.
4. Johnson's term for the kind of society he wanted
6. The surrounding air, earth, water; Johnson backed laws to protect this
8. Johnson became president after this man's death.
10. Johnson's home state
12. At one time, Johnson was _____ leader in the House.
13. Initials shared by Johnson, his wife, and his daughters

Johnson and his family all had similar names: Lyndon Baines, Lady Bird, Lynda Bird, and Luci Baines.

**JOHNSON
1963–1969**

Word List

anti	City	Great	LBJ	riots
assassination	employment	health	legislature	teacher
Bird	environment	horse	majority	Texas
	grandfathers	Kennedy	Nam	

RICHARD M. NIXON

"I am not a crook," Richard M. Nixon insisted when people accused him of lying. But it turned out that he was guilty in the worst presidential scandal in history, known as "Watergate."

Nixon's accomplishments before Watergate form a long list. As a young senator from California, he was picked to be Dwight Eisenhower's vice president. In that position, Nixon traveled the world on diplomatic missions. He lost a close presidential election to John Kennedy, then lost another election for California governor. He told the press that they wouldn't "have Nixon to kick around any more," but Nixon never gave up easily. Within six years, he had been elected president.

President Nixon's first priority was ending the war in Vietnam. He began a program, which he called "Vietnamization" of the war. American soldiers were slowly brought home as the bombing of North Vietnam was intensified and South Vietnamese soldiers were given training. Finally, Nixon got a cease-fire agreement signed with North Vietnam and pulled the last Americans out of the region. However, the North and South continued to fight until 1975, when the North won.

Nixon helped arrange a cease-fire between Israel and its Arab neighbors, Egypt and Syria. He was the first president to visit communist China. Back home, he tackled rising prices with federal wage and price controls—a daring move.

In 1972, Nixon was easily reelected, but during the campaign five agents of CREEP, the Committee to Re-Elect the President, were caught burglarizing Democratic National Committee headquarters at the Watergate apartment complex in Washington, D.C. Nixon claimed he knew nothing about it, but the scandal grew as the Senate Watergate Committee took evidence in televised hearings. The turning point came when the Supreme Court ordered Nixon to turn over tape recordings he had made. The tapes proved he had lied and covered up illegal actions. Nixon resigned on August 9, 1974. He was pardoned by the new president, Gerald Ford, soon afterward.

Across

1. After losing two major elections, Nixon told the press they would not have him to _____ around any more.
3. Last name of president who pardoned Nixon
8. Acronym (first letters) for the Committee to Re-Elect the President
9. Nixon's term for turning over the war to Vietnam
11. Part of Vietnam that won the war
12. Nixon staff members stole records from this political party.
14. Kind of missions Nixon made abroad for Eisenhower
16. Kind of animal Checkers was
17. Nixon helped arrange a cease-fire between Israel and Syria and _____.

Down

Nixon gave a famous speech in which he denied taking gifts in return for favors, and stated that he was going to keep Checkers, a dog he had been given.

2. Nixon was the first president to visit this communist country.
4. Nixon decided to do this when evidence showed he was guilty.
5. Nixon's home state
6. Nixon was accused of lying and covering __ crimes done by his staff.
7. Term used for the Nixon scandal
8. Nixon daringly placed these on wages and prices to keep them down.
10. Court that ordered Nixon to turn in his tapes
13. Recordings; those made by Nixon put him in a bad light
15. Nixon said, "I am not a _____."

**NIXON
1969–1974**

Word List

California	CREEP	dog	North	up
China	crook	Egypt	resign	Vietnamization
controls	Democratic	Ford	Supreme	Watergate
	diplomatic	kick	tapes	

53

GERALD R. FORD AND JIMMY CARTER

Gerald R. Ford of Michigan was minority leader (leader of the Republicans) in the House of Representatives when Richard Nixon asked him to replace Spiro Agnew as vice president. Agnew had resigned after being accused of income tax cheating and accepting bribes. Nixon wanted a man with a reputation for honesty, and he got one. The Senate and House approved Nixon's choice, as is called for in the Twenty-fifth Amendment to the Constitution.

When Nixon resigned because of the Watergate scandal, Ford became president. Ford was the first person to take this office without ever having been elected president or vice president. Soon after he became president, Ford gave Nixon a full pardon, absolving him of any crimes he may have committed. This move angered many people and damaged Ford's chances in the next presidential election.

In 1976, newcomer Jimmy Carter was elected. James Earl Carter, who preferred to be called Jimmy from childhood on, sold peanuts while growing up in Plains, Georgia. Carter had been governor of Georgia for one term but had no national government experience. Carter had high ideals and a relaxed, personable leadership style. He supported human rights around the world and pushed for environmental protection and arms control.

Carter's greatest success in foreign policy was the signing of the 1979 Camp David Accords, which brought peace between Israel and Egypt. He also arranged for Panama to receive control of the Panama Canal in 1999. Just before the last year of Carter's presidency, Americans at the U.S. embassy in Tehran were taken hostage by a group of Iranian revolutionaries. The hostages were not released until the day Carter left office. The prolonged hostage crisis, along with a limping economy, caused Carter to lose his bid for a second term.

Jimmy Carter has continued to do diplomatic work since retiring from office. He has helped supervise free elections around the world and worked to provide housing for the poor in the United States.

Across

2. Carter arranged to turn control of the Panama Canal over to this country.
4. _____ of Representatives; where Ford was serving when Nixon asked him to be vice president
6. Vice President Agnew was accused of income ___ cheating.
7. Carter lost reelection partly because this was in bad shape.
9. Replacement of the vice president is covered by the Constitution's Twenty-fifth _____.
12. Two-letter abbreviation for Ford's home state
14. State where Carter served as governor
15. Carter helped establish peace between Egypt and _____.
16. Carter helped build many of these for the poor.

Down

James Earl Carter, a country boy, was known as Jimmy from childhood on.

1. Carter's peace agreements between Israel and Egypt were called the ____ David Accords.
3. Ford served as vice president under him.
4. In foreign affairs, Carter emphasized this kind of rights.
5. Carter was unable to free the American ones held in Iran.
7. Carter has helped supervise these worldwide since retiring.
8. Carter's formal first name
10. Same as 12 Across
11. What Carter sold in Georgia
13. Last name of Nixon's first vice president

FORD
1974–1977

CARTER
1977–1981

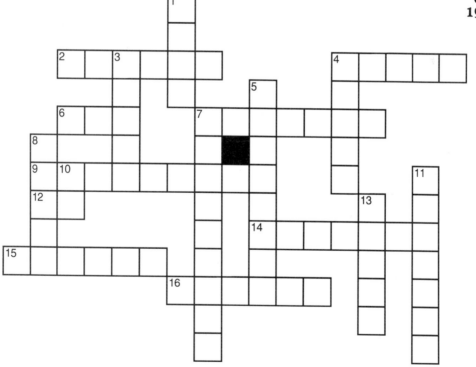

Word List

Agnew	economy	House	James	Panama
Amendment	elections	houses	MI	peanuts
Camp	Georgia	human	MI	tax
	hostages	Israel	Nixon	

RONALD REAGAN

Ronald Reagan grew up in Illinois. While working as a radio sportscaster in Iowa, Reagan traveled to California. There, he took a Hollywood screen test and soon began making movies. He became a famous actor, working in films for nearly twenty-eight years. During the 1950s, he worked as a spokesman for General Electric, hosting a television show and giving speeches.

California Republicans noticed Reagan and asked him to run for governor. During his two terms as governor, Reagan cut down the number of people on welfare. He criticized university students who were protesting and cut funds for higher education.

Reagan was elected president in 1980, winning such popularity with his speeches that the press called him "the Great Communicator." He cut taxes while increasing defense spending, which led to a record-high national debt. He urged Congress to support anticommunist movements in Nicaragua, Angola, and elsewhere around the world. In 1983, he sent U.S. troops to overthrow the government of the tiny island of Grenada. Although Reagan built up arms, he also met with Soviet leader Gorbachev in a series of summit meetings, easing relations with the Soviet Union.

Scandal struck Reagan's administration when it was revealed that U.S. officials had sold arms to Iranian kidnappers in exchange for American hostages being held in Lebanon. In addition, profits from the arms sales had gone to the Nicaraguan "contras," a group of people who were rebelling against their government, in spite of Congress's decision not to support the contras. Reagan had pledged never to negotiate with terrorists. Reagan claimed he had nothing to do with the Iran-contra affair, but many people on his staff were involved.

At the end of Reagan's second term, the economy was strong. Despite the earlier scandal, Reagan left office as one of the most popular presidents of the century. A few years later, Reagan announced that he had been diagnosed with Alzheimer's disease, an incurable illness that leads to loss of memory.

Across

1. Last name of Reagan's press secretary, paralyzed by shots aimed at the president
4. This improved in the second half of Reagan's presidency.
7. Reagan held summit meetings with this Soviet leader.
11. Reagan once gave speeches for _____ Electric.
12. Reagan's favorite candy
15. The contras were in this country.
16. People working for the president; Reagan blamed them for the Iran-contra affair
17. While governor of California, Reagan spoke against these people.
18. Two-letter abbreviation of the state where Reagan started working as an actor

Down

Reagan's press secretary, Jim Brady, was paralyzed in an assassination attempt on the president. From his wheelchair, Brady works tirelessly for gun control.

2. Money owed; Reagan increased this for the nation
3. Alzheimer's disease causes loss of this.
5. Reagan was called "the Great _____."
6. Films; Reagan acted in them
8. In California, Reagan cut down on this aid to the needy.
9. Three-letter abbreviation of Reagan's home state
10. Reagan increased spending on this.
13. The Iran-contra affair centered on profits gained from selling these.
14. Term for a rebel fighting against the Nicaraguan government

**REAGAN
1981–1989**

Jelly beans were a favorite Reagan snack in the White House.

Word List

arms	Communicator	economy	jelly beans	staff
Brady	contra	General	memory	students
CA	debt	Gorbachev	movies	welfare
	defense	Ill.	Nicaragua	

GEORGE BUSH

"Read my lips: no new taxes!" That's what George Bush promised when he was running for president. He was a Republican through and through, and he thought government should do less, not more.

Bush grew up in a wealthy Connecticut family. After a stint as a navy pilot during World War II and studying law at Yale University, he moved to Texas to enter the booming oil business. He made a small fortune there and was elected to the House of Representatives. Presidents Nixon and Ford gave him a series of important jobs: ambassador to the United Nations, chair of the Republican National Committee, chief of the U.S. Liaison Office in China, and director of the Central Intelligence Agency. Then, in 1981, he became Ronald Reagan's vice president. After two terms, he was easily elected as Reagan's successor to the presidency.

As president, Bush had to deal with a Democratic Congress. He signed a budget bill that reduced the amount the government had to borrow, but the bill also increased taxes, contrary to Bush's promise. The president had better luck in foreign affairs. The old Soviet Union was crumbling, a change that some people said was due to the triumph of American-style free enterprise. In the Persian Gulf, Iraqi leader Saddam Hussein tried to take over the tiny, oil-rich nation of Kuwait. Bush organized allies and sent troops to turn him back. The war was over quickly, with few lives lost.

The popularity Bush enjoyed at the end of the Gulf War faded as the economy drooped. Bush did not have any workable solutions to the problem of high unemployment. He lost the next election, leaving office after only one term.

Across

2. Two-letter abbreviation of the state where Bush grew up
3. George Bush made money from this natural resource.
5. Bush served as chair of the Republican _____ Committee.
9. Lack of jobs; a problem that cost Bush his job
13. First name of Bush's wife
14. Bush's job during World War II
15. Bush was elected to the House from this state.
16. Number of terms Bush served as president
17. Number of terms Bush was vice president

Down

1. Name of the Bush dog that supposedly wrote its memoirs
2. Bush was chief of the U.S. office in this Asian country.
4. First name of the Iraqi leader during the Gulf War
6. Country invaded by Iraqi forces

7. Bush's first national budget reduced the amount the government had to _____.
8. Initials of the Central Intelligence Agency, once headed by Bush
10. Bush said "Read my ___" for emphasis.
11. University where Bush studied law
12. During his campaign, Bush promised not to raise these.

**BUSH
1989–1993**

Barbara Bush with her dog Millie, the supposed author of a popular book Barbara actually wrote

Word List

Barbara	CIA	Millie	pilot	two
borrow	CT	National	Saddam	unemployment
China	Kuwait	oil	taxes	Yale
	lips	one	Texas	

BILL CLINTON

William Jefferson Clinton, often called Bill, spent most of his childhood in Hot Springs, Arkansas, where he did well in school and learned to play the saxophone for fun. Clinton graduated from Georgetown University, attended Oxford University as a Rhodes scholar, and received a degree from Yale Law School before returning to Arkansas. There, he taught law and won his first election, as state attorney general. He then became governor on and off for several terms before he ran for president as a Democrat.

Clinton won the presidential election partly because he favored a center path between traditional Republican and Democratic ideas. In his first term, Clinton pushed for NAFTA, the North American Free Trade Agreement, which linked Mexico, Canada, and the United States, allowing companies and products to move freely across borders. Many Republicans favored this agreement, while some traditional Democrats did not.

Bill Clinton's health-care reform program did not pass through Congress. Clinton was criticized for placing his wife, Hillary, in charge of the effort. In 1996, Clinton signed an important welfare reform bill, which required people on welfare to seek work. And by the middle of his second term, there was a federal surplus—the first in a generation.

In foreign affairs, Clinton's attention turned to the former Yugoslavia, where ethnic groups clashed. In 1995, following a peace agreement, Clinton sent U.S. troops to Bosnia to keep the peace. Later, Serbs attacked ethnic Albanians in the neighboring province of Kosovo. This time, Clinton argued for a bombing campaign to stop Serb leader Slovodan Milosevic. The bombing succeeded, but many lives were lost. Clinton also played an important part in the Middle East peace agreement made between Israel and the Palestinians in 1993.

Clinton, no stranger to scandal, may be best remembered as the second president to be impeached, or formally accused of a crime. He was charged with lying under oath about his relationship with Monica Lewinsky. The young woman was a White House aide with whom Clinton had an improper sexual relationship. At the Senate trial, Clinton was found not guilty of "high crimes and misdemeanors," in the language of the Constitution. Clinton apologized to the nation and returned to his job.

Across

1. First name of Clinton's wife
5. Clinton served in this position just before he became president.
8. Clinton was found not guilty of "high crimes and _____."
10. Last name of Serb leader who tried to take over Kosovo
11. Clinton's formal first name
12. Clinton had hoped to reform the way people pay for this type of care.
13. Province where the United States and its allies stopped a Serb takeover
14. Absence of conflict; American troops were sent to enforce it in Bosnia

Down

President Clinton with his wife, Hillary Rodham Clinton, one of the most active first ladies in U.S. history, right before his first inauguration

2. Two-letter abbreviation of Clinton's home state
3. Major conflicts occurred in Bosnia and Kosovo, located within this former country.
4. Neither far left nor far right; describes Clinton's politics
6. Initials of the North American Free Trade Agreement
7. Clinton taught this in Arkansas.
8. Clinton hosted the _____ East peace agreement between Israel and the Palestinians.
9. Short name for musical instrument Clinton plays
10. First name of White House aide involved in scandal with Clinton
11. Under Clinton's law, people who get welfare money must now seek this.

CLINTON 1993–

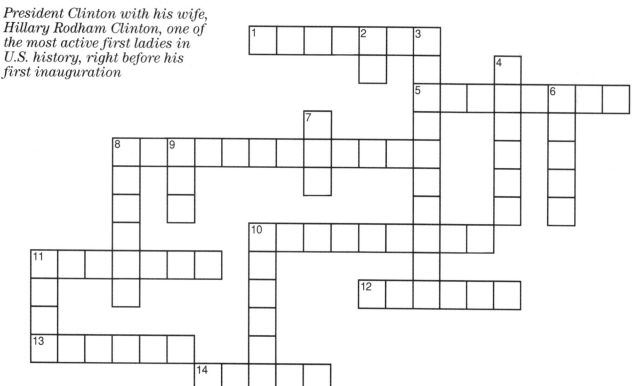

Word List

ÁR	health	Middle	NÁFTA	work
center	Hillary	Milosevic	peace	Yugoslavia
governor	Kosovo	misdemeanors	sax	
	law	Monica	William	

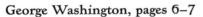

ANSWERS

George Washington, pages 6–7

```
                    F R A N C E
      V I R G I N I A T H       F
    T       E       T   S       A
  C H A I R M A N   H   E       R
  C L N     E       E   E L E C T O R S
H A M I L T O N   E U T R   T       M
B   I       I   A   R     H O R S E E
I   N   M A   T A     R           S
N       A   T A X   L
G E N E R A L R A L
      R
    W H I S K E Y
      A
```

John Adams, pages 8–9

```
            O   M         L
            N A B I G A I L
        F R A N C E   W   Y
      W   E   S       J
H     H   I N D E P E N D E N C E   P O E T
A     I   R   A   H   J       E
R   V I C E   F A R M   U       R
V   T         L   L E G I S L A T U R E
A R O T U N D I T Y   E       R   I
D             S       T       O   G
                  M A S S A C R E   H T
```

Thomas Jefferson, pages 10–11

```
            D
        M D E       V
R E P U B L I C A N A
    L A   L       M
    A N   W A R   B   A R M Y
V   T         R   A   O
F I F T Y   A D A M S   F   E
I   C     L W   T   P U R C H A S E Y
C   E     M O N T I C E L L O R
E               N   W   D O
            S M A L L
```

James Madison, James Monroe, and John Q. Adams, pages 12–13

```
        F E E L I N G       A
    S   L     O             N
    T C O N S T I T U T I O N   T
P A R T Y   R   M   E S       H
O   A E C O N I D A     D O L L E Y
T   T         T H S       M
D O C T R I N E   O     B
O   M C     G     N     I
J A C       R   E N G L I S H     W A
          S   E   A L L I G A T O R
          S P A I N
```

Andrew Jackson, pages 14–15

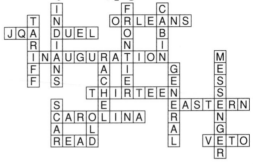

```
    I       F     C
  T I N     O R L E A N S
J Q A R   D U E L O   B
  R I F   I N A U G U R A T I O N   M
  I F F   N S     A C I E     G   E
  C             E   T H I R T E E N S
  F           S       A   E A S T E R N
            C A R O L I N A   R     G
            R E A D         A L   V E T O
                            L       R
```

Martin Van Buren, William H. Harrison, and John Tyler, pages 16–17

```
D               S T A T E S
E           S L   C O   W
V P R E S T I P P E C A N O E   M O N T H
  R E     E   E     I   N O   H
  E   D U T C H     T E X A S M I
  S   S   M S       I   N   P   G
  I L L   S E       Z   S N A T I O N A L
K I N D E R H O O K E         L     A N D
  O               L           K
                              A
```

James Polk, Zachary Taylor, and Millard Fillmore, pages 18–19

```
          D A
        N A R
    C O M P R O M I S E
    A L I       K       C O N G R E S S
    L I F       R           I       T
A   I F O R E G O N F U G I T I V E O
O R E G O N     R   W A T E R N M A C
M   R N I     W A   E D       E A Z
Y   N I     C A N A D A     D   L   H
    I A     D Y             A D
    S L A V E R Y             L A W N
```

Franklin Pierce and James Buchanan, pages 20–21

```
        N
    R E P U B L I C A N     S L A V E
  N   W     L               E Z N
  O     D E M O C R A T I C   E D D
  R     E           H       D E
  T     E           A
N H E R C H R I S T M A S
  E   U           N
  R   B   G A D S D E N
K A N S A S       S
            S C O T T
            O   M
          N I E C E
```

Abraham Lincoln, pages 22–23

Andrew Johnson and Ulysses S. Grant, pages 24–25

Rutherford B. Hayes, James A. Garfield, and Chester A. Arthur, pages 26–27

Grover Cleveland, pages 28–29

Benjamin Harrison and William McKinley, pages 30–31

Theodore Roosevelt, pages 32–33

William H. Taft, pages 34–35

Woodrow Wilson, pages 36–37

Warren G. Harding and Calvin Coolidge, pages 38–39

Herbert Hoover, pages 40–41

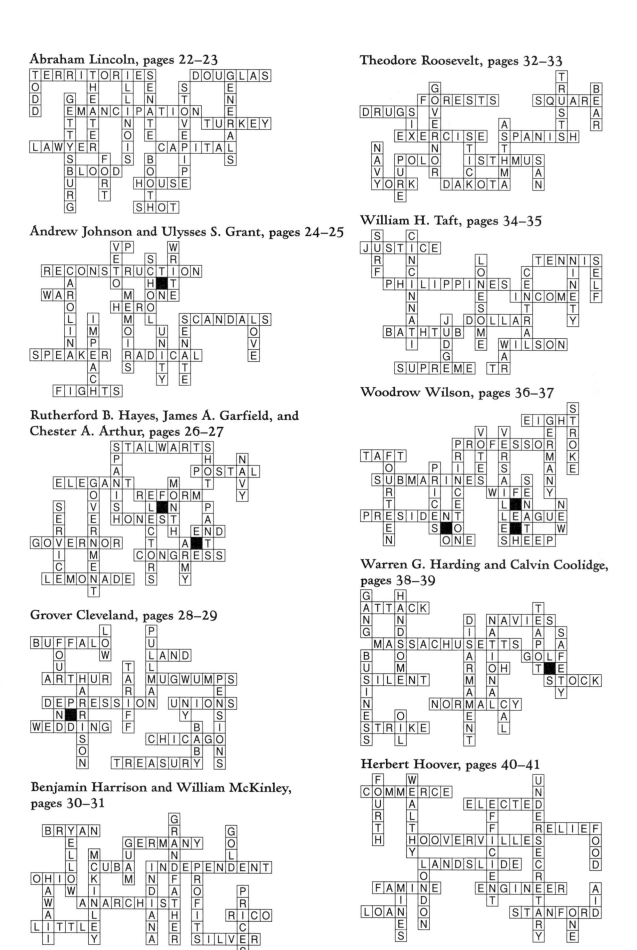

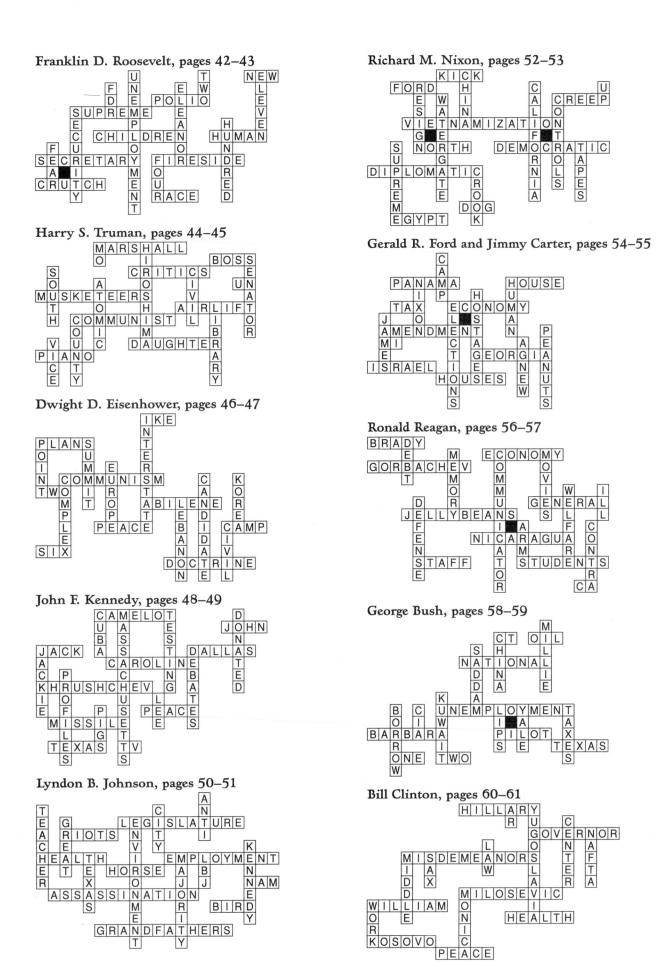

Franklin D. Roosevelt, pages 42–43

Harry S. Truman, pages 44–45

Dwight D. Eisenhower, pages 46–47

John F. Kennedy, pages 48–49

Lyndon B. Johnson, pages 50–51

Richard M. Nixon, pages 52–53

Gerald R. Ford and Jimmy Carter, pages 54–55

Ronald Reagan, pages 56–57

George Bush, pages 58–59

Bill Clinton, pages 60–61